BRIDESMAIDS'
COLORING AND
ACTIVITY BOOK

Sandy Creek
NEW YORK

Contents

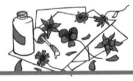

Congratulations!

You have been lucky enough to be chosen as a bridesmaid. The excitement has already started and you're going to feel just like a princess in your pretty dress.

This book is bursting with fun stuff for you to do before the wedding, on the day itself while the grown-ups are busy, and after the day is over. There's plenty of room to record all your memories, too.

From the cake to the confetti, the flowers to the photographs, get ready for a wonderful wedding day!

A Special Card

Show the bride how much it means to you to be her bridesmaid
by giving her a handmade thank you card.

You will need: • 2 pieces of white 8 ½ × 11 in card • 1 piece of green 8 ½ × 11 in card
• 2 more pieces of card in any flower shades you like • a ruler • a pencil • scissors • glue
• pencils or markers in different shades.

1. Fold the two pieces of white card in half to become the outside and inside of your card.

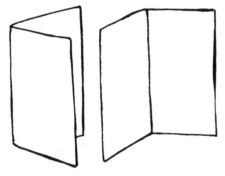

2. Take one piece and cut a diagonal line about 2 inches long on the folded edge to make a flap. Fold the flap down along the dotted line, then unfold it again.

Fold

4. On the green card, draw two stem shapes at least 2 inches long and cut them out. Draw and cut out some leaf shapes as well.

5. On the flowery shades of card, draw and cut out two flower shapes.

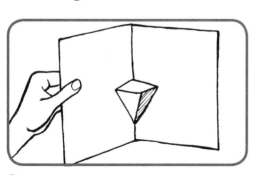

3. Open the card and pull the flap inside towards you to make a pop-out vase shape.

6. Glue the stems to the back of the flowers and glue the leaves to the stems. Glue the bott of each stem to the inside of the vase shape.

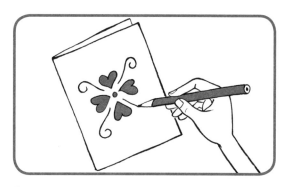

7. When the glue is dry, fold the inside in half again and glue the other folded card to the outside of it.

8. Decorate the front of your card with pencils or markers, and write a special message inside.

Thanks a bunch ...

... for asking me to be your bridesmaid.

Being A Brilliant Bridesmaid

You have been asked to be a bridesmaid, and that means
you have an exciting and important job ahead.
Follow these top tips to be a shining star on the big day.

Relax

A wedding is for everyone to enjoy, but it's
natural to be a bit nervous beforehand.

If you can, find a quiet spot to sit down.
Then take some long, slow, deep breaths in
through your nose and out through your
mouth to help you get instant calm.

Remember

If you have duties, such as
helping to hold the bride's train,
don't wander off until you've
done your part.

Unsure of what you should
be doing? Ask an adult – they
will be happy to help.

Glide

Stand up straight and walk elegantly down the aisle.
Imagine there is an invisible string coming out of the very top
of your head and pulling you up towards the sky.

For real grace, look straight ahead, not at your toes.

The most important thing is to remember to smile:
a bridesmaid's dress just doesn't match a frowning face.

Walking with a small book on your head is good practice for your graceful glide. Can you keep it in place?

Have Fun!

There is always a lot going on at
a wedding, but don't let that get
in the way of the main point:
to have a really happy day!

Doodle some dream outfits
for these beautiful bridesmaids.

Now draw yourself in your bridesmaid's dress.

Don't forget to include all the details of your dress and
hair, so you'll always remember feeling like a princess.

9

Puzzle Love

Can you solve these lovely puzzles?
Turn to page 126 to check your answers.

Wedding Sudoku

Complete the grid so that each row, each column, and each block of four squares contains a ring, a bouquet, a gift, and a heart.

Gorgeous Gifts

There's a little gift for you mixed up with the wedding gifts. Can you spot it?
It's in a square box with a striped ribbon, wrapped in paper with hearts on it.

Last-Minute Maze

Rosie has to get from her house to the church in time for the wedding.
Can you get her there safely, dodging bad weather and traffic jams,
but picking up two presents and the bouquet on the way?

Start

Church

Confetti Corner

Once the bride and groom have tied the knot, it's traditional to shower them with confetti.

Read on to find out how to make your own special supply.

Make Your Own Confetti

You will need: • tissue paper in different shades • scissors • a pencil.

1. Fold a sheet of tissue paper in half over and over again until you have lots of layers, but can still cut through all of them with scissors.

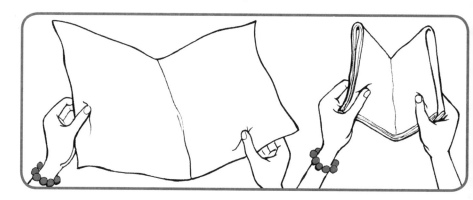

2. Holding the folds as flat as you can, draw small hearts on the top layer.

3. Carefully cut out the hearts through all the layers.

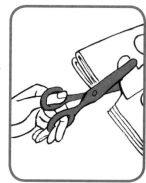

4. Throw away the outside part to leave lots of tissue hearts. Repeat, using tissue in different shades.

Cute Confetti Container

Turn the page and doodle decorations for the inside of your container, then follow the instructions below.

You will need: • scissors • glue
• pencils or markers in different shades.

1. Decorate the shape below with flowers and hearts, using bright pencils or markers.

2. Cut along all the solid lines, then fold along all the dotted lines, keeping this side on the outside.

3. Put some glue on the gray circles and pinch each pair together to make the corners of the container. (The pinched flaps will be on the inside.)

4. Close the container by slotting the two halves of the circle of hearts together, as shown below.

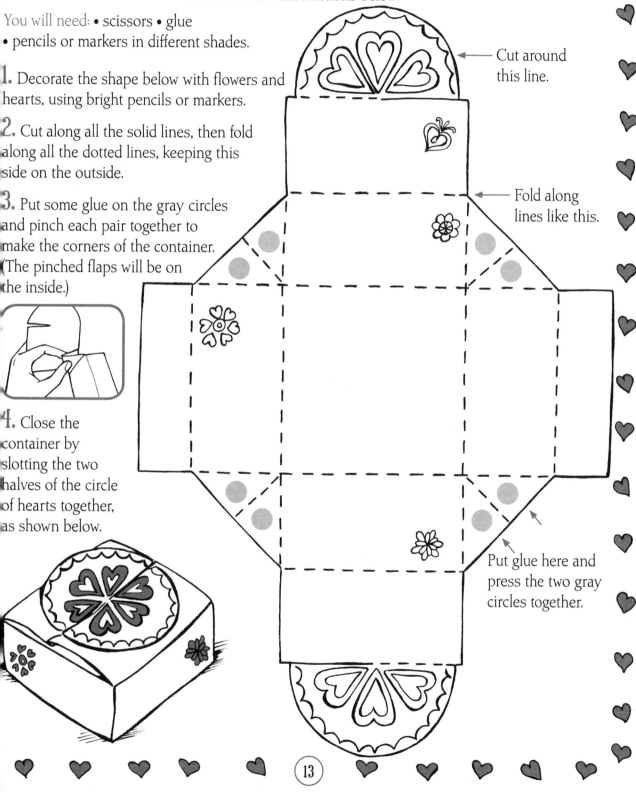

Cut around this line.

Fold along lines like this.

Put glue here and press the two gray circles together.

Confetti comes in all shapes and sizes. Fill the space with fun confetti ideas. (They will form the inside of your confetti container on page 13.)

Wedding Detective

You'll need sharp eyes for these puzzles.
Check your answers on pages 126 and 127.

Shoe Shuffle

Choosing shoes is a tricky business, and these ones
have got all mixed up. Can you pair them up again and
find which one is still single? The first one has been
done for you.

Family Photo Facts

Look carefully at this wedding picture, then answer the questions below.

A. How many people have a beard? ☐

B. How many are wearing glasses? ☐

C. How many people have more than one flower? ☐

D. How many have flowers in their hair? ☐

Picture Puzzles

Use your bridesmaid brainpower to make sense
of these puzzling portraits.

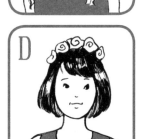

Smile, Please!

These proud parents want to take photos of the bridesmaids before the wedding. Can you work out which happy snapper took each of the pictures on the right? Check your answers on page 127.

A

B

C

D

E

F

Train Trail

The flower girls are trying to spot how many lacy shapes they can see in the bride's train. Try it yourself.

Turn to page 127 to find out if you are right.

Why not fill the shapes in as you count them?

	Flowers		Hearts
	Squares		Stars
	Diamonds		

Wedding Day Fun

Weddings bring out the best in people – and the worst!
Try these crazy puzzles and check your answers on page 127.

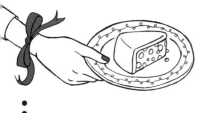

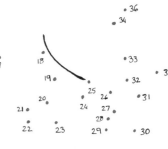

Dotty Dora

There's an extra special
bridesmaid at this wedding.
Join the dots to discover the
bride's best friend.

What A Hat!

This guest has chosen a humongous hat for her niece's
wedding, but which of the shadows below belongs to it?

Marriage Mayhem

Three pieces of this puzzle have been removed and mixed up with some others.
Can you work out which are the missing pieces of this wedding-party disaster jigsaw?

A

B

C

D

E

F

Wedding Cake Creations

Why not share your wedding fever by making some mini wedding cakes to share with your friends? Here's how:

You will need: • a pack of 12 plain cupcakes • a small, round cookie cutter • a pack of powdered sugar • a small jug of water • a small bowl • food dye • a teaspoon • cake decorations, such as sprinkles and chocolate chips.

1. Take six cakes and carefully push the cookie cutter into the top of each one. With a bit of wiggling, you can pull out a cutter-shaped mini cake. (Put the cakes with holes in them to one side – you don't need them.)

2. Follow the instructions on the sugar pack to make some frosting.

3. Add a tiny bit of food dye to the frosting to give you a pretty pastel shade.

4. Using the back of a teaspoon, frost the six whole cakes.

5. Place a mini cake on the top of each frosted cake. Gently push it into the frosting, so it stays in place.

6. Smooth some more frosting over the top layer of your mini wedding cake and then cover each one in yummy cake decorations.

Now dig in and enjoy your gorgeous handiwork!

Doodle delicious decorations on this wedding cake picture.

These balloons are far too plain for a party.
Add your own doodle decorations to brighten them up.

Matchmaker

Help! There's more than one wedding happening at a huge hotel. Can you match the mixed-up brides and grooms? One has been done for you. See page 127 to check your answers.

Bridesmaid Bingo

Add extra fun to the wedding by playing bingo with other bridesmaids and friends.

Bridesmaid Bingo is a game for three players. Cut around the dotted lines of the gift boxes and tokens on the opposite page. Now you're ready for some bingo fun.

Wedding List

Photo Album

Clock

Candles

Fruit Bowl

Kettle

Cushion

Frying Pan

Vase

Coffee Pot

Rug

Picture Frame

Lamp

1. One player should be the "bride" and the other two players her "bridesmaids." The bride has a list of gifts she hopes to receive from her guests (here on the left).

2. The bridesmaids each take one of the gift boxes and sets of counters. One will use the counters with hearts on the back, and one will use the counters with flowers.

3. Each bridesmaid chooses six of her twelve gifts to place face-up in the squares in her gift box. The bride must not be able to see them.

4. The bride then calls out items from her wedding list, in any order. Each time a bridesmaid has a matching item in her gift box, she must hand it over to the bride.

5. The winner is the bridesmaid who empties her gift box first.

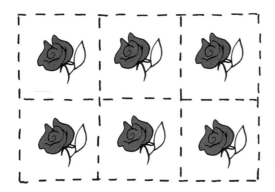

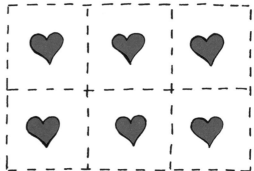

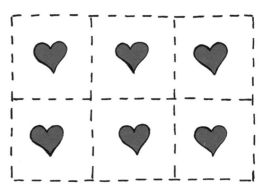

Wacky Weddings

Some people choose a traditional wedding. Others make sure their day is like no other wedding in the world.

Love Is In The Air

Many people would be terrified of jumping out of a plane, but one bride and groom decided that was the perfect way to tie the knot. Hand in hand, this couple got married while sky-diving!

Kiss And Fries

One couple loved their burgers so much, they decided to get married in their local fast-food restaurant. Who knew that burgers could be so romantic?

A Hoppy Couple

In northwestern India, two frogs were married in front of 2,000 wedding guests. An ancient tradition said that this would help to end water shortages. The bride and groom spent their honeymoon in a stream. Sadly, neither of them turned into a prince.

Deeply In Love

In a Hong Kong water park, a wedding took place underwater. The bride even wore a long, white dress with her diving gear.

What's Your Flower Fashion Style?

The type of bouquet you would love to carry
is a real clue to your personal style. Take this quiz and find out
what your choice of blooms says about your look.

Start
What size would your perfect bouquet be?

As big and bold as possible.

What shape is your bouquet?

Trailing and pretty.

Which of these bouquets would suit you best?

Neat and round.

What kind of flowers would go best with your outfit?

A small and delicate bunch.

What would you choose to tie the stems?

A ribbon made of lace.

A twirling strand of ivy.

Which of these flower choices do you prefer?

A beautiful bunch of dainty white and pink flowers.

Traditional Beauty

You are a girl with elegance and grace, who loves the look of a traditional white wedding. You like clothes that are classy and cool.

A bold bouquet of brilliant red blooms – the brighter the better.

Top Trendsetter

You like to wear outfits that make you stand out from the crowd. You create your own style and love to have fun with your clothes.

A bouquet in a contrasting shade, maybe even crazily clashing.

Blooms carefully chosen in the same shades as your clothes.

Perfect Princess

The style you love is pretty and girly. Wearing the look you like best makes you feel confident and happy with the world.

Lots of different kinds of flowers all in the same shade.

Fashion Queen

You are always interested in the coolest trends and like to be dressed in the very latest style. You love to keep changing your look.

A fabulous mix of show-stopping shades and blooms.

A Fabulous Feast

One of the best parts of a wedding is the food. Can you draw and label some of the delicious delights?

Dream Menu

What would you serve guests at your
own wedding or another special celebration?
Fill in the menu with all the foods you like best.

MENU

Napkin Origami

Origami is the Japanese art of folding paper.
Have fun after your celebration meal by using your napkin
to make this pretty origami heart.

You will need: • a square paper napkin (but a cloth one works, too).

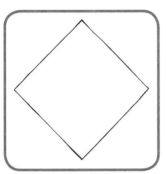

1. Open out a square paper napkin and place it like this, with the pattern, if there is one, underneath.

2. Fold the top corner down to meet the bottom corner and press along the fold with your fingers to make it crisp. Open the napkin out again.

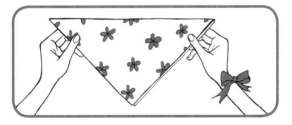

3. Fold the corner on the right to meet the corner on the left and press along the fold again. Then open the napkin out.

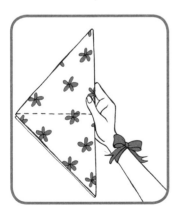

4. Fold the top corner down to meet the center fold.

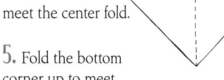

5. Fold the bottom corner up to meet the top edge at the center fold.

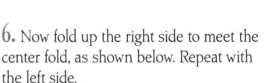

6. Now fold up the right side to meet the center fold, as shown below. Repeat with the left side.

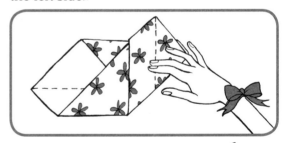

7. Turn the napkin over.

8. Fold the top points and the sides along the lines shown here, then turn the shape over.

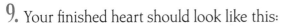

9. Your finished heart should look like this:

If your napkin heart is made of paper, why not write a message on it and give it to someone you love?

Heart To Heart

Someone has been busy making hearts from patterned napkins. Which two of the hearts below have exactly the same pattern? Check your answer on page 127.

A    B    C    D

E    F    G   H

Do You Dare?

How many of these wedding challenges do you dare to take on?
Have a competition with friends to see if you are the bravest bridesmaid.
If one of you fails a challenge, it's time for a forfeit!

Go on to the dance floor when it is empty and dance by yourself for at least 20 seconds.

Forfeit: you must promise to do another player's dare for them later.

Tell three people, keeping a straight face, that you have always wanted to change your name to Silver Van Sausage the Second.

Forfeit: you must give away half your dessert or wedding cake.

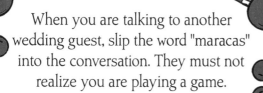

When you are talking to another wedding guest, slip the word "maracas" into the conversation. They must not realize you are playing a game.

Forfeit: tell everyone the most embarrassing moment of your life.

Be completely silent for three whole minutes.

Forfeit: you must pay each of the other players a compliment.

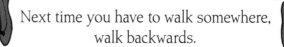

Next time you have to walk somewhere, walk backwards.

Forfeit: try to touch your nose with your tongue.

Picture This!

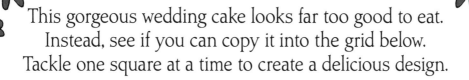

This gorgeous wedding cake looks far too good to eat.
Instead, see if you can copy it into the grid below.
Tackle one square at a time to create a delicious design.

True Or False?

There are lots of different wedding customs. Can you guess
which of these are true traditions and which are false?
Check your answers on page 127.

A It is said that if the groom trips over as he walks the bride down the aisle, he will catch a cold on the honeymoon.

B Many people believe that the person who catches the bride's bouquet when she tosses it over her shoulder will be the next to get married.

C Some people say that if it rains the Tuesday before the wedding, it will rain all day during the ceremony.

D It is said that if the bride strokes a cat three times on the night before her wedding, she will have a happy marriage.

E Some people believe that if you put a slice of wedding cake under your pillow at night, you will dream of your future husband.

Picture Perfect

Here are two pictures of a happy couple at their beautiful Hindu wedding. Can you spot five differences between the pictures? The answers are on page 128.

Hindu brides often have pretty patterns painted on their hands with henna.
Doodle some more heavenly henna patterns below.

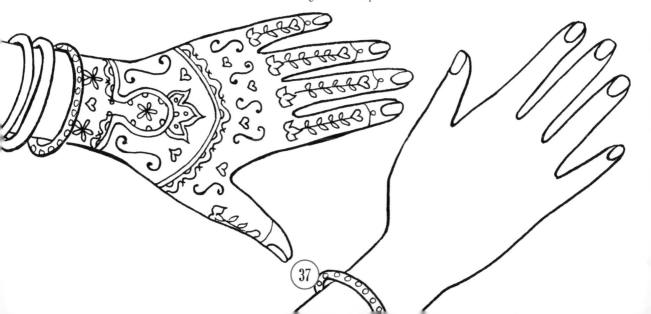

Super Snooper

How much can you find out about the bride and groom?
Make it your mission to fill out this fun fact file.

The full name of the bride is:

_____

The full name of the groom is:

_____

The bride and groom met for
the first time on:

_____

at:

_____

_____

The highlight of the day
for the bride is:

_____

_____

The highlight of the day
for the groom is:

_____

_____

The groom's earliest memory is:

_____

_____

Top Tip

Those closest to the couple will have all the lowdown, so get help from their friends and family throughout the day.

Their pet names for each other are:

_____

_____

_____

On their first date, the couple went to:

_____

_____

"Their song" is:

_____

_____

_____

One word to sum up the day:

From the bride: _____

From the groom: _____

The bride's earliest memory is:

_____

_____

_____

The bride and groom have known each other for:

_____

_____ years and

_____ months

Getting-To-Know-You Games

There may be people at the wedding you have never met before. Why not have fun playing these games and make some new friends?

I Love, She Loves . . .

This is a game for four or more people.

1. Sit down in a circle.

2. One person starts off the game by telling the group what their name is and something interesting about him- or herself, for example, "My name is Emma and I love swimming."

3. The next person to the left does the same, but also repeats what the first person said, such as, "My name is Hannah and I love chocolate cake, and this is Emma and she loves swimming."

4. Continue like this until everyone has had a turn. If someone forgets, the person they have forgotten can try to help by miming, but they mustn't speak.

☆ *Top Tip* ☆

Give the game a cheeky twist by changing "I love" to "I hate" and letting new friends know your dislikes, too.

Would You Rather?

This is another good game for four or more people.

1. First, line up, one behind the other, with one person, "the leader," facing the rest.

2. The leader asks a "Would you rather ...?" question, for example, "Would you rather eat cake (pointing to the left) or chocolate (pointing to the right)?", and you must jump to the left or right.

3. Then line up again and give another person a turn as the leader.

Stuck for questions? There are some good ideas in the box below to get you started.

Would you rather ...

☆ ... become invisible or be able to fly?
☆ ... be an astronaut or an actor?
☆ ... drink lemonade or a milkshake?
☆ ... watch a movie or watch TV?
☆ ... be an orange or an apple?
☆ ... be world famous or a millionaire?

Dancing Diva

Show everyone else how it's done on the dance floor!
With these dance moves, you'll really get the party started.
A few minutes' practice is all you need.

The Cross Wiggle

1. Put your right arm out in front of you, then your left.

2. Turn your right hand palm up, then do the same with your left hand.

3. Put your right hand on your left shoulder, then your left hand on your right shoulder.

4. With your arms still crossed, bend your knees and wiggle down, then up again.

The Side Clap

1. Step to the left with your left foot.

2. Bring your right foot up beside your left foot and clap your hands to the left.

3. Now step right, close up your left foot and, at the same time, clap to the right.

4. Keep making those moves, bridesmaid!

The Shoulder Shrug

1. Start with your legs. Staying in one place, tap your right toe on the floor, then put it down flat again. Do the same with your left foot.

2. Now add some arm movements. As you tap your right foot, touch your right shoulder with your left hand, as if you were brushing something off it. Shrug the shoulder.

3. You guessed right! As you tap your left foot, brush your left shoulder with your right hand – and shrug. Keep on dancing!

The wedding disco is in full swing.
Decorate these dancers' outfits, and turn them all shades of crazy!

Wedding Treasure Hunt

If you have some time to fill between feasting and dancing, why not try this treasure-hunt teaser? Get some fellow bridesmaids or friends on the hunt, too, and see who can hunt down the most items.

You will need: • a pen or pencil • up to nine competitors.

Name	Coin	Comb	Flower	Lipstick	Cake	Man's Sock

How To Play

Write your name and your competitors' names in the first column. Each person puts a tick in their row under an object when they find it. The winner is the one who finds the most. (Don't forget to put everything back where you found it at the end.)

Top Tip

Why not ask relatives and friends to look in their pockets and purses to help you find all the objects you need?

	Photograph	Candy	Camera	Wedding Invitation	Travel Ticket	Ribbon	Something Pink

The World Of Weddings

There are lots of wonderful wedding traditions. Can you guess where these customs began? Draw a line from the custom to its country's flag. The first one has been done for you. Check your answers on page 128.

China

A

In this country it is traditional for wedding dresses to be bright red, as this is thought to bring good luck.

India

Germany

B

The couple place garlands around each other's necks as part of the ceremony.

C

The bride is carried "over the threshold" (through the door) of her new home by the groom.

D

The wedding cake is called a croquembouche (crunchy in the mouth). It is made of choux buns piled up in a tall tower.

France

United Kingdom

E

Wedding guests pin presents of paper money to the happy couple's clothes.

F

Guests eat Hochzeitssuppe (wedding soup), which is made from chicken.

Greece

Wedding Wishes

Here's a space to help you remember other guests at the wedding.
Ask them to write wishes and messages in the shapes,
or they can simply sign their names. Why not add your own doodle
decorations for even prettier pages?

The Bride and Groom's signatures.

⭐ Table-Top Tricks ⭐

Impress other guests with these cunning magic tricks.
With a little practice, you will wow with your mysterious skills.
Remember though, a proper magician never reveals her secrets ...

The Vanishing Salt Shaker

You will need: • a large napkin • a salt shaker • a coin.

1. Tell your audience you will make a salt shaker and a coin disappear before their very eyes.

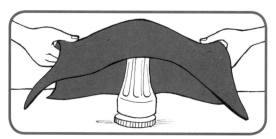

2. Place the coin on the table and put the salt shaker on top. Drape the napkin over both.

3. Say, "On three, the coin and the napkin will disappear. One ... two ... three!"

4. Quickly lift the salt shaker inside the napkin, but make a big show of staring at the coin on the table. Secretly drop the salt shaker into your lap, while you say, "Oops! The coin is still there. But the salt shaker ...

5. ... isn't!" At that moment, put the napkin (still shaped as if around the salt shaker) back on the table and slam your other hand down on it. Wow! The salt shaker has "disappeared"!

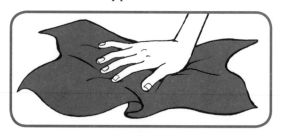

The Magic Napkin

1. Before you start, secretly open up a napkin and crumple it into a ball.

2. Hold the ball in your hand all the time until the end of the trick as shown. Keep your hand relaxed, as below, so it doesn't look as if you are clutching something.

From the front

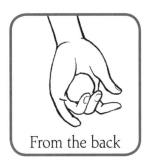
From the back

3. Announce that you can make a torn-up napkin whole again. Keeping the crumpled napkin hidden, make a big show of opening and tearing up the other napkin.

4. Use your fingers to squeeze the torn pieces into a ball. Don't get the two balls mixed up!

5. Close your hand around both balls, keeping your thumb on the torn-up one, and shake your hand high and low, pretending to "magic" the pieces together. Drop the torn-up ball secretly into your lap.

6. Now, before your audience's amazed eyes, slowly unfold the remaining napkin and listen to them gasp as they see that it is whole!

Your Future Love

Try this little bit of magic and you just might get a sneaky peek into your own romantic future ...

You will need: • an apple with the stalk attached.

Now, follow the instructions below:

Hold the apple in one hand and with the other hand start gently twisting the stalk around and around. As you twist, say the letters of the alphabet out loud.

The letter you are saying when the stalk breaks off is the first initial of your true love.

Start saying the alphabet again from the beginning. As you do so, gently start poking it into the apple at different places.

The letter you are saying when the stalk breaks through the skin of the apple will be the second initial of your future love.

The Bride's Bouquet

After the wedding ceremony, it's traditional for the bride to throw her bouquet. It's said that the girl who catches it will be the next to be married.

Who catches this bouquet and who only grabs a leaf or a flower? Turn to page 128 to see if you are right.

Anna

Bella

Carla

Davina

The Wedding That Nearly Wasn't!

Finish Belinda's adventure by drawing the final scene.

The sun was shining when Belinda woke up. Perfect! It was her sister Marie's wedding day, and Belinda was going to be a bridesmaid.

Belinda was dressed and helping Marie get ready when the phone rang.

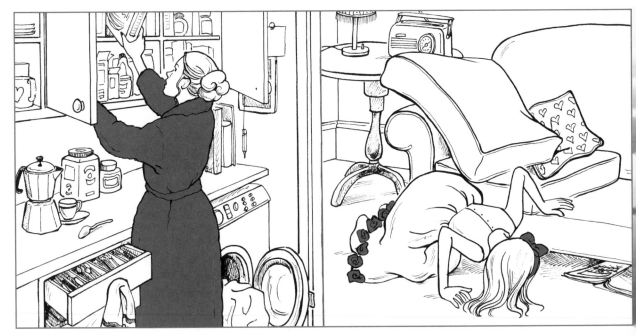

Belinda and Marie searched the whole house.

Suddenly, out of the corner of her eye, Belinda spotted the culprit ... and the missing rings!

Would they get to the church on time? Or was the wedding ruined?

The wedding was perfect, thanks to Belinda.

Flower Power

Don't let your wedding memories fade with your flowers.
Keep your petals perfect with the art of flower pressing.

You will need: • a selection of wedding flowers • a pile of heavy hardcover books
• white paper • glue • a pretty picture frame.

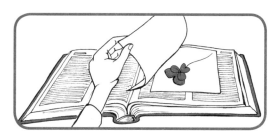

1. While the flowers are still fresh, take a heavy book and open it in the middle.

2. Place a sheet of paper on the right-hand page to protect the book.

3. Take one flower and lay it carefully on the sheet of paper, making sure the petals are nicely arranged.

4. If there is room, put more flowers on the paper, but make sure there is space between them.

5. Place another piece of paper on top of the flowers and close the book.

6. Repeat this with more books and flowers, until you have pressed all your best blooms.

7. Put more books on top of the flower-filled books – or anything heavy you can find – and leave them for at least two weeks.

. When you open the books, you should find that your flowers are dried and delicate. Be very careful when you lift them from the paper.

. Arrange the flowers on a piece of card or paper that will fit your frame, then glue them in position to create a gorgeous reminder of your day as a bridesmaid.

Top Tips

Don't press very large and full flowers, such as roses. Take the petals off and press them one by one. They'll look lovely.

White flowers look best displayed on a darker card.

Make greeting cards and bookmarks with your flowers. Transparent contact paper on top will keep them safe.

Doodle pretty pressed-flower decorations on the bookmark, card, and label.

Bookmark

Card

Label

Getting Away

Planning a wedding is exhausting. No wonder the bride and groom need a holiday! Try these honeymoon travel puzzles, then check your answers on page 128.

Whose Honeymoon?

Can you match the newlyweds with the honeymoon they have chosen?
The first one has been done for you.

A

B

C

D

1

2

3

4

Parting Puzzle

A huge hotel can have so many corridors it's easy to get lost.
Help the happy couple and their guests to find their way
from the ballroom to their waiting car.

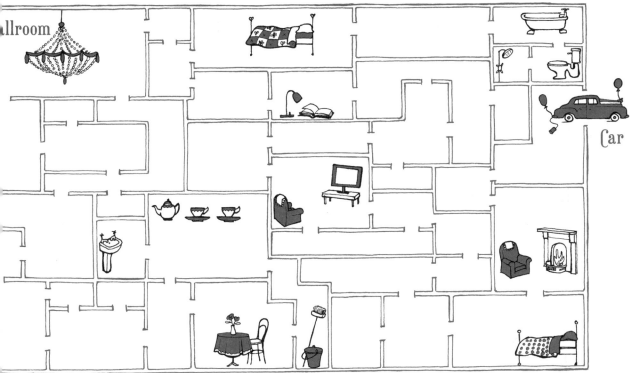

Before the bride and groom leave, decorate this wedding car with balloons,
tin cans, streamers — whatever you like!

Making Wedding Memories

Use these pages to keep a record of important facts about the big day. They will help you remember these magical moments forever.

The Ceremony

Who is getting married?

_____ and _____

How do you know them?

_____

What is the date of the wedding?

_____

Where is the ceremony taking place?

_____

What time does it begin?

_____

The Weather

Tick the boxes and fill in the thermometer.

- ☐ sunny
- ☐ cloudy
- ☐ rainy
- ☐ windy
- ☐ snowy

very hot

hot

warm

cold

very cold

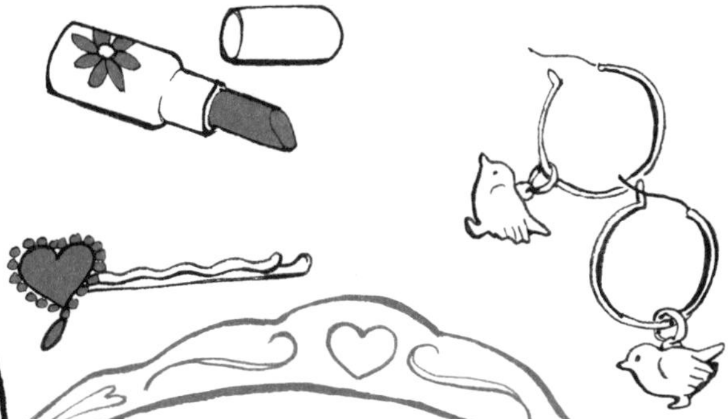

Getting Ready

Fill in the spaces so you remember important people and details.

Helping me get dressed: _____

_____

Doing my hair: _____

Funny things to remember: _____

_____

On The Way . . .

Make a note of your travel arrangements.

_____

To the wedding by _____

with _____

From the wedding by _____

with _____

Wedding Map

All The Answers

Puzzle Love
pages 10 and 11

Wedding Sudoku

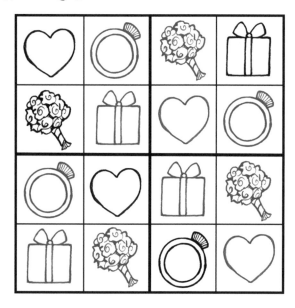

Last-Minute Maze

Wedding Detective
page 15

Shoe Shuffle

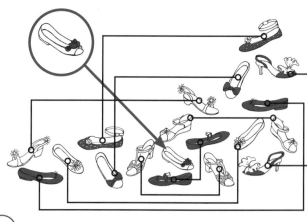

Gorgeous Gifts

Family Photo Facts

A. 2 people have a beard.
B. 3 people are wearing glasses.
C. 5 people have more than one flower.
D. 6 people have flowers in their hair.

Picture Puzzles
pages 16 and 17

Smile, Please!

Proud parent 1 took photo F.
Proud parent 2 took photo A.
Proud parent 3 took photo D.
Proud parent 4 took photo E.
Proud parent 5 took photo C.
Proud parent 6 took photo B.

Train Trail

There are 19 flowers.   There are 16 hearts.
There are 14 squares.   There are 19 stars.
There are 16 diamonds.

Wedding Day Fun
pages 18 and 19

Dotty Dora

She is a bridesdog!

What A Hat!

Shadow F is the correct one.

Marriage Mayhem

Pieces A, B, and D complete the puzzle.

Matchmaker
page 23

Bride A and Bridegroom 4 belong together.
Bride B and Bridegroom 1 belong together.
Bride D and Bridegroom 2 belong together.
Bride E and Bridegroom 3 belong together.

Napkin Origami
page 33

Heart To Heart

Hearts B and H are the same.

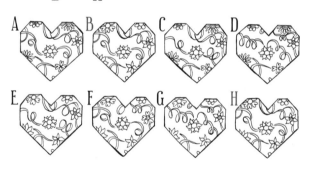

True Or False?
page 36

A. False.
B. True. Some girls scramble to catch it!
C. False.
D. False.
E. True.

Picture Perfect
page 37

The World Of Weddings
pages 46 and 47

B. Couples traditionally give each other garlands in India.

C. The groom traditionally carries the bride over the threshold in the United Kingdom.

D. A croquembouche wedding cake is traditional in France.

E. Guests pin money on the couple's clothes in Greece.

F. Hochzeitssuppe is traditionally eaten at a wedding in Germany.

Your Future Love
page 53

The Bride's Bouquet

Carla catches the bride's bouquet.

Getting Away
pages 58–59

Whose Honeymoon?

Beach honeymoon **B** belongs to couple **4**.
Skiing honeymoon **C** belongs to couple **1**.
Sailing honeymoon **D** belongs to couple **3**.

Parting Puzzle

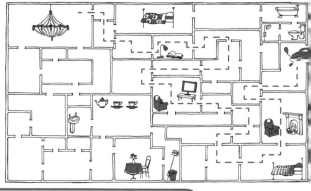

An Imprint of Sterling Publishing
387 Park Avenue South
New York, NY 10016

SANDY CREEK and the distinctive Sandy Creek logo are registered trademarks of Barnes & Noble, Inc

© 2012 Buster Books

This 2013 custom edition is published exclusively for Sandy Creek by Buster Books, an imprint of Michael O'Mara Books Limited.

Illustrated by Ann Kronheimer. Edited by Nicola Baxter and Hannah Cohen.
Designed by Barbara Ward and Amy Cooper. Cover design by Angie Allison.

ISBN: 978-1-4351-4724-9

Manufactured by Wing King Tong Paper Products Co., Ltd., China

Lot #:
2 4 6 8 10 9 7 5 3 1
04/13